The Three
allow even the
a reperto
Simply by mastering the   used in any of these
songs, you really could play in a day...perhaps even less!
And once you know them, you're on the way to being a
fully-fledged performer.
This songbook doesn't use musical notation, instead you just
learn three easy-to-read chord boxes.
Many popular songs only use the three chords.
The most common formula is the 'three-chord-trick',
using the three primary chords of any major key.
So in G this would be G, C and D.
Many rock'n'roll numbers and Dylan's folk-inspired
songs use only these chords.

Three Chord Tricks

Throughout the book chord boxes are printed at the
head of each of song; the chord changes are shown
above the lyrics. It's left up to you, the guitarist,
to decide on a strum rhythm or picking pattern.
You might find the pitch of the vocal line is not always
comfortable because it is pitched too high or too low.
In that case, you can change the key without learning
a new set of chords; simply place a capo
behind a suitable fret.
Whatever you do, this three-chord songbook
guarantees hours of enjoyment for
the prospective guitarists.

Relative Tuning

The guitar can be tuned with the aid of pitch pipes or dedicated electronic guitar tuners which are available through your local music dealer. If you do not have a tuning device, you can use relative tuning. Estimate the pitch of the 6th string as near as possible to E or at least a comfortable pitch (not too high, as you might break other strings in tuning up). Then, while checking the various positions on the diagram, place a finger from your left hand on the:

5th fret of the E or 6th string and **tune the open A** (or 5th string) to the note (A)

5th fret of the A or 5th string and **tune the open D** (or 4th string) to the note (D)

5th fret of the D or 4th string and **tune the open G** (or 3rd string) to the note (G)

4th fret of the G or 3rd string and **tune the open B** (or 2nd string) to the note (B)

5th fret of the B or 2nd string and **tune the open E** (or 1st string) to the note (E)

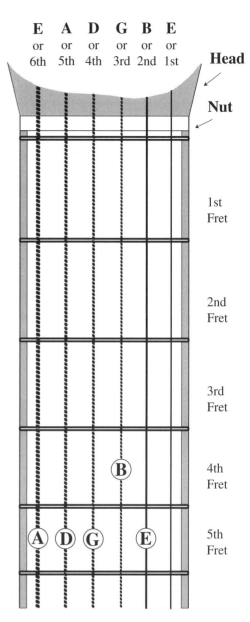

Reading Chord Boxes

Chord boxes are diagrams of the guitar neck viewed head upwards, face on as illustrated. The top horizontal line is the nut, unless a higher fret number is indicated, the others are the frets.

The vertical lines are the strings, starting from E (or 6th) on the left to E (or 1st) on the right.

The black dots indicate where to place your fingers.

Strings marked with an O are played open, not fretted.

Strings marked with an X should not be played.

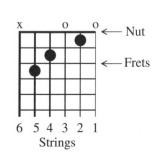

4

Got The Feelin'

Words & Music by
Richard Stannard, Julian Gallagher, Sean Conlon, Jason Brown & Richard Breen

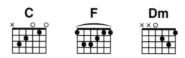

Intro

‖: C　　　　F
Na na na, na — na na,
C　　　F
Na na na, na — na na na. :‖ *Play 4 times*

Verse 1

C　　　　　F
Here we go again with the beats,
　　　　　　　　　C　　　　　　　　　　F
We got your heads boppin' now you're talking from your seats.
　　　　　　　　　C
If this is what you're wantin' over there,
F
Throw your hands up in the air,
　　　　　　　C　　　　　　　F
Because you know we bring the sound so unique.
　　　　　　C　　　　　F
Now ev'rybody's movin' 'n' ev'rybody's groovin',
　　　　　　　C　　　　　F
Gettin' down with Five when we come your way.
　　　　　C　　　　　　　F
Move it to the left, now you shake it to the right,
　　　　　　　　　C　　　　　　　　F
Because you know we gotta keep this party boppin' through the night.

Check me out. Yo!

Pre-chorus 1

C　　　　　F
Seven six five four three two one,
　　C　　　　　　　　F
I'm on the microphone, got ya hot like the sun.
　　　C　　　　　　　F
So a-one two three, now I'm waiting on the four,
C　　　　　　　F
Kick down the door and turn it up a little more.

Chorus 1

       C   F
If you've got the feelin', jump up to the ceilin',

       C   F
Oh, we're gettin' down tonight.

        C   F
And one if you're gonna, two if you wanna,

        C   F
Three 'cos ev'rything's alright.

        C   F
If you've got the feelin', less of the dreamin',

      C   F
Oh, we're gettin' down tonight.

        C   F
It's just 'round the corner, tell me if you wanna,

      C   F
Five will make you feel alright.

Link | C   F | C   F ||

Verse 2

C   F
Move it at the back to the track,

          C   F
We got it going on, we're the leaders of the pack.

          C
And if you feel alright, hold it tight,

F
See we wanna carry on,

          C   F
'Cos we're gonna take you through into the dawn.

           C   F
Now everybody's movin', everybody's groovin',

          C   F
Gettin' down with Five when we come your way.

          C   F
So raise up your arms, as we drop it on the one,

              C   F
You see we're gonna carry on because the fun has just begun.

Check us out. Yo!

Pre-chorus 2   As Pre-chorus 1

Chorus 2   As Chorus 1

C Dm C Dm   C Dm C Dm
Oh, _____   oh, _____

	C	F
Middle	Na na na, na __ na na,	

C   F
Na na na, na __ na na,

C   F
Na na na, na __ na na na.

C   F
Na na na, na __ na na,

C   F
Na na na, na __ na na na.

C   F
Na na na, na __ na na,

C   F
Na na na, na __ na na na.

C   F
Na na na, na __ na na,

C   F
Na na na, na __ na na na.

Chorus 3

            C   F
If you've got the feelin', jump up to the ceilin',

         C   F
Oh, we're gettin' down tonight.

           C   F
And one if you're gonna, two if you wanna,

         C   F
Three 'cos ev'rything's alright.

          C   F
If you've got the feelin', less of the dreamin',

         C   F
Oh, we're gettin' down tonight.

         C   F
It's just 'round the corner, tell me if you wanna,

         N.C.
Five will make you feel alright.

Chorus 4   As Chorus 1

Chorus 5   As Chorus 3

All Together Now

Words & Music by
John Lennon & Paul McCartney

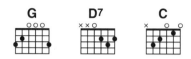

Intro   ‖: G | G | G | G   :‖

Verse 1
G
One, two, three, four,
D7
Can I have a little more?
G   D7
Five, six, seven, eight, nine, ten,
            G
I love you.

Verse 2
(G)
A, B, C, D,
D7
Can I bring my friend to tea?
G   D7
E, F, G, H, I, J,
            G
I love you.

Pre-chorus 1
(G)   C
(Bom, bom, bom, bompa bom.)

Sail the ship,
G
(Bompa bom) chop the tree,
C
(Bompa bom) skip the rope,
D7
(Bompa bom) look at me!

Chorus 1

             G
(All together now) all together now,

(All together now) all together now,
             D7
(All together now) all together now,
             G
(All together now) all together now.

Verse 3

(G)
Black, white, green, red,
D7
Can I take my friend to bed?
G   **D7**
Pink, brown, yellow, orange and blue,
     G
I love you.

Chorus 2 & 3 ‖: As Chorus 1 :‖

Pre-chorus 2

G   **D7**   **G**   **C**
(Bom, bom, bom, bompa bom.)

Sail the ship,
G
(Bompa bom) chop the tree,
C
(Bompa bom) skip the rope,
D7
(Bompa bom) look at me!

Chorus 4 & 5 ‖: As Chorus 1 :‖

Chorus 6

             G
(All together now) all together now,

(All together now) all together now,
            D7
(All together now) all together now,
       (D7)   **G**
(All together now) all together now.

Calling Elvis

Words & Music by
Mark Knopfler

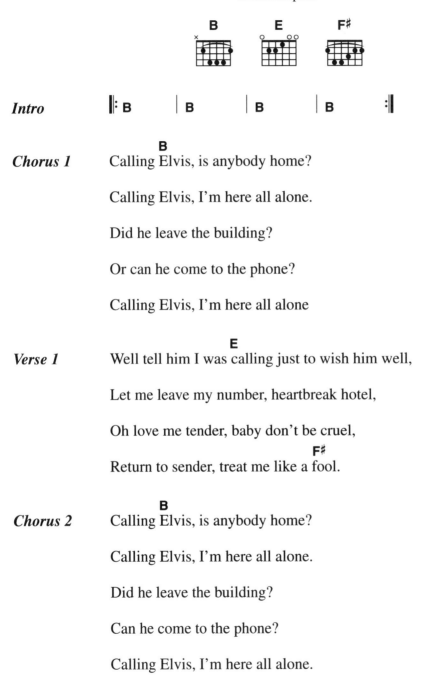

Intro ‖: B | B | B | B :‖

Chorus 1

B
Calling Elvis, is anybody home?

Calling Elvis, I'm here all alone.

Did he leave the building?

Or can he come to the phone?

Calling Elvis, I'm here all alone

Verse 1

E
Well tell him I was calling just to wish him well,

Let me leave my number, heartbreak hotel,

Oh love me tender, baby don't be cruel,

F♯
Return to sender, treat me like a fool.

Chorus 2

B
Calling Elvis, is anybody home?

Calling Elvis, I'm here all alone.

Did he leave the building?

Can he come to the phone?

Calling Elvis, I'm here all alone.

| *Solo 1* | ‖: B | \| B | \| B | \| B | :‖ |

B
Chorus 3 Why don't you go get him, I'm his biggest fan.

You gotta tell him, he's still the man.

Long distance baby, so far from home,

Don't you think maybe you could put him on.

E
Verse 2 Well tell him I was calling just to wish him well,

Let me leave my number, heartbreak hotel,

Oh love me tender, baby don't be cruel,

                                F♯
Return to sender, treat me like a fool.

B
Chorus 4 Calling Elvis, is anybody home?

Calling Elvis, I'm here all alone.

Did he leave the building?

Or can he come to the phone?

Calling Elvis, I'm here all alone.

| *Solo 2* | \| N.C. | \| N.C. | \| |
| ‖: B | \| B | \| B | \| B | :‖ *Play 3 times* |

Chorus 5 As Chorus 4

| *Coda* | ‖: B | \| B | \| B | \| B | :‖ *Repeat to fade* |

11

Cruel Summer

Words & Music by
Steve Jolley, Tony Swain, Siobhan Fahey, Keren Woodward & Sarah Dallin

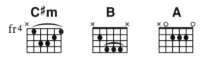

Intro

C#m B   A B C#m
    Mm, _____

B   A B C#m
Ah, _____

B   A B C#m
Mm, _____

B   A B
Ah, _____

Verse 1

C#m
Hot summer streets

B   A   B
And the pavements are burning,

  C#m B A B
I sit around

C#m   B   A
Trying to smile, but the air

        B   C#m B A B
Is so heavy and dry.

Verse 2

C#m   B   A
  Strange voices are singing,

    B   C#m
Ah, what did they say?

      B A   B A B
Things I can't understand.

  C#m   B
It's too close for comfort,

     A   B   A B A B
This heat has got right out of hand.

Chorus 1

        C♯m   A   B   A
It's a cruel, (cruel,) cruel summer,

C♯m   A   B
   Leaving me here on my own.

A   C♯m   A   B
It's a cruel, (it's a cruel,) cruel summer,

A   C♯m
Now you're gone.

        A   B
You're not the on - ly one.

A   (C♯m) (A) (C♯m) (A)
It's a cruel.

Verse 3

        C♯m   B
The city is crowded,

        A
My friends are away,

B   C♯m   B A B
And I'm on my own.

      C♯m   B
It's too hot to handle,

      A   B   A B   A B
So I _ gotta get up and go,   up and go. _____

Chorus 2

        C♯m   A   B   A
It's a cruel, (cruel,) cruel summer,

C♯m   A   B
   Leaving me here on my own.

A   C♯m   A   B
It's a cruel, (it's a cruel,) cruel summer,

A   C♯m
Now you're gone.

        A   B
You're not the only one.

        C♯m   A   B
It's a cruel, (cruel,) cruel summer,

A   C♯m   A   B
(Leaving me,) leaving me here on my own.

A   C♯m   A   B
It's a cruel, (it's a cruel,) cruel summer,

A   C♯m
Now you're gone.

        A   B
You're not the on - ly one.

A   C♯m
It's a cruel…

B   A   B   N.C.
  Mm, _____ ah.

Middle

<pre>
     C#m   A   B
        Now don't you leave me, mm,
                     A
     Now don't you leave me,
     C#m   A
        Now don't you leave me.
           B   A
     Come on, come on.
     C#m   A   B
        Now don't you leave me, mm,
                     A
     Now don't you leave me,
     A   B
        Now don't you leave me,
           A   B
     Come on, come on.
</pre>

Chorus 3

<pre>
              C#m   A   B
     It's a cruel, (cruel,) cruel summer,
     A   C#m   A   B
     (Leaving me,) leaving me here on my own.
     A   C#m   A   B
     It's a cruel, (it's a cruel,) cruel summer,
     A   C#m
     Now you're gone.
            A   B
     You're not the on - ly one.
     A   C#m   A   B   A C#m A
     It's a cruel, (cruel,) cruel summer,
           B   A   C#m
     It's a cruel summer.
                  A   B   A C#m A
     (It's a cruel,) cruel summer,
           B   A   C#m
     It's a cruel summer.
</pre>

Get Up, Stand Up

Words & Music by
Bob Marley & Peter Tosh

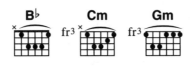

Intro | B♭ Cm | B♭ ||

Chorus 1

Cm
Get up, stand up: stand up for your rights!

Get up, stand up: stand up for your rights!

Get up, stand up: stand up for your rights!

Get up, stand up: don't give up the fight.

Verse 1

Cm
Preacherman, don't tell me,

Heaven is under the earth.

I know you don't know

What life is really worth.

It's not all that glitters is gold;

'Alf the story has never been told:

So now you see the light, eh!

Stand up for your rights. Come on!

Chorus 2

Cm   **Gm B♭**
‖: Get up, stand up: stand up for your rights!
Cm   **B♭**
Get up, stand up: don't give up the fight!   :‖

Verse 2

Cm
Most people think,

Great God will come from the skies,

Take away everything

And make everybody feel high.

But if you know what life is worth,

You will look for yours on earth:

And now you see the light,

You stand up for your rights. Jah!

Chorus 3

Cm
Get up, stand up! (Jah, Jah!)

                      Gm   B♭
Stand up for your rights! (Oh-hoo!)

Cm
Get up, stand up! (Get up, stand up!)

                B♭
Don't give up the fight! (Life is your right!)

Cm
Get up, stand up! (So we can't give up the fight!)

              Gm   **B♭**
Stand up for your rights!   (Lord, Lord!)

Cm
Get up, stand up! (Keep on struggling on!)

                B♭
Don't give up the fight! (Yeah!)

Verse 3

Cm
We sick an' tired of-a your ism-skism game,

Dyin' 'n' goin' to heaven in-a Jesus' name, Lord.

We know when we understand:

Almighty God is a living man.

You can fool some people sometimes,

But you can't fool all the people all the time.

Cm
So now we see the light, (What you gonna do?)

We gonna stand up for our rights! (Yeah, yeah, yeah!)

So you better:

Coda

Cm
Get up, stand up! (In the morning! Git it up!)
                                   Gm   **B**♭
Stand up for your rights! (Stand up for our rights!)
Cm
Get up, stand up!
                                        B♭
Don't give up the fight! (Don't give it up, don't give it up!)
Cm
Get up, stand up! (Get up, stand up!)
                                 Gm   **B**♭
Stand up for your rights! (Get up, stand up!)
Cm
Get up, stand up!
                              B♭
Don't give up the fight! (Get up, stand up!)

‖: **Cm**
Get up, stand up!

Stand up for your rights! :‖ *Repeat to fade*

Going Down

Words & Music by
Ian Brown & John Squire

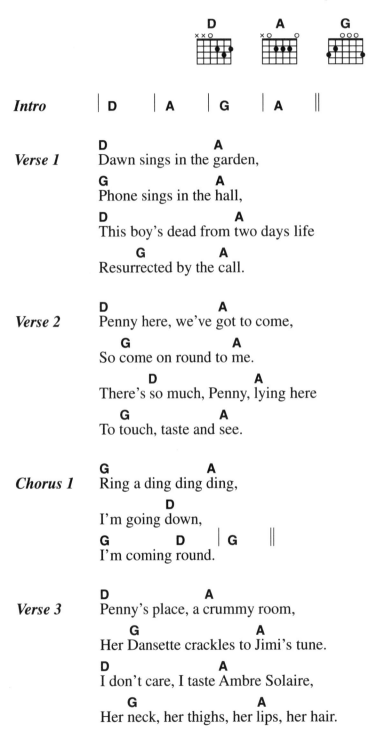

Intro　　　| D 　| A 　| G 　| A 　||

Verse 1

D　　　　　　　A
Dawn sings in the garden,

G　　　　　　　A
Phone sings in the hall,

D　　　　　　　　　A
This boy's dead from two days life

　　　　G　　　　　　A
Resurrected by the call.

Verse 2

D　　　　　　　　　A
Penny here, we've got to come,

　　G　　　　　　　A
So come on round to me.

　　　　　　D　　　　　　A
There's so much, Penny, lying here

　　G　　　　　　A
To touch, taste and see.

Chorus 1

G　　　　　　　A
Ring a ding ding ding,

　　　　　　D
I'm going down,

G　　　　　D　　| G　　||
I'm coming round.

Verse 3

D　　　　　　　A
Penny's place, a crummy room,

　　　　G　　　　　　　A
Her Dansette crackles to Jimi's tune.

D　　　　　　A
I don't care, I taste Ambre Solaire,

　　　G　　　　　　　A
Her neck, her thighs, her lips, her hair.

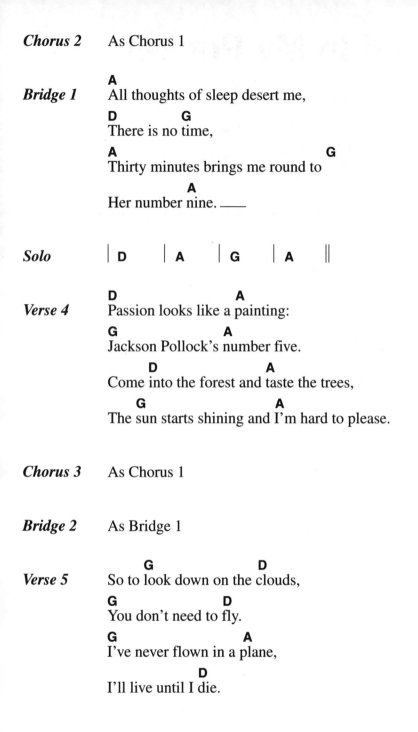

Chorus 2   As Chorus 1

              A
Bridge 1   All thoughts of sleep desert me,
              D   G
              There is no time,
              A   G
              Thirty minutes brings me round to
                          A
              Her number nine. ____

Solo | **D** | **A** | **G** | **A**   ‖

              D   A
Verse 4   Passion looks like a painting:
              G   A
              Jackson Pollock's number five.
                     D   A
              Come into the forest and taste the trees,
                G   A
              The sun starts shining and I'm hard to please.

Chorus 3   As Chorus 1

Bridge 2   As Bridge 1

                  G   D
Verse 5   So to look down on the clouds,
              G   D
              You don't need to fly.
              G   A
              I've never flown in a plane,
                          D
              I'll live until I die.

Hand In My Pocket

Words by Alanis Morissette
Music by Alanis Morissette & Glen Ballard

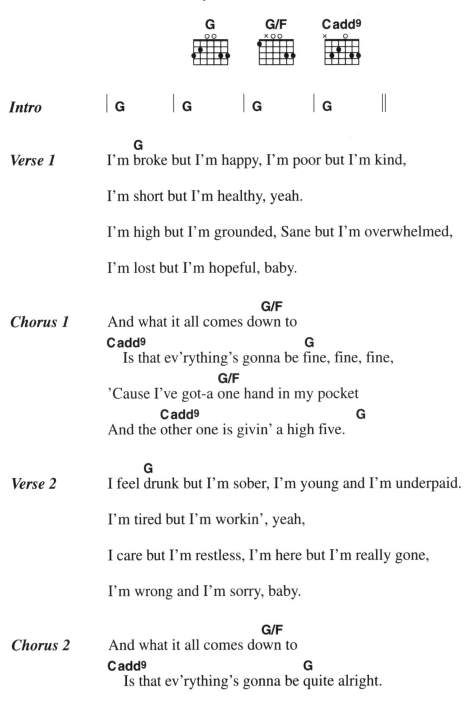

Intro | G | G | G | G ||

Verse 1

       G
I'm broke but I'm happy, I'm poor but I'm kind,

I'm short but I'm healthy, yeah.

I'm high but I'm grounded, Sane but I'm overwhelmed,

I'm lost but I'm hopeful, baby.

Chorus 1

                           G/F
And what it all comes down to
Cadd⁹   **G**
   Is that ev'rything's gonna be fine, fine, fine,
                      G/F
'Cause I've got-a one hand in my pocket
           Cadd⁹   **G**
And the other one is givin' a high five.

Verse 2

       G
I feel drunk but I'm sober, I'm young and I'm underpaid.

I'm tired but I'm workin', yeah,

I care but I'm restless, I'm here but I'm really gone,

I'm wrong and I'm sorry, baby.

Chorus 2

                           G/F
And what it all comes down to
Cadd⁹   **G**
   Is that ev'rything's gonna be quite alright.

cont.

> **G/F**
> 'Cause I've got-a one hand in my pocket
> **Cadd⁹**   **G**
> And the other one is flickin' a cigarette.

Solo   ‖: **G** | **G** | **G** | **G**   :‖

Chorus 3

> **G/F**
> And what it all comes down to
> **Cadd⁹**   **G**
> Is that I haven't got it all figured out just yet.
> **G/F**
> 'Cause I've got-a one hand in my pocket
> **Cadd⁹**   **G**
> And the other one is givin' a peace sign.

Verse 3

> **G**
> I'm free but I'm focused, I'm green but I'm wise,
>
> I'm hard but I'm friendly, baby.
>
> I'm sad but I'm laughing, I'm brave but I'm chicken shit,
>
> I'm sick but I'm pretty, baby.

Chorus 4

> **G/F**
> And what it all comes down to
> **Cadd⁹**   **G**
> Is that no one's really got it figured out just yet.
> **G/F**
> 'Cause I've got-a one hand in my pocket
> **Cadd⁹**   **G**
> And the other one is playin' a piano.

Chorus 5

> **G/F**   **Cadd⁹**
> And what it all comes down to my friends, yeah,
> **G**
> Is that ev'rything's just   fine, fine, fine,
> **G/F**
> 'Cause I've got-a one hand in my pocket
> **Cadd⁹**   **G**
> And the other one is hailing a taxi cab.

Outro   ‖: **G** | **G** | **G** | **G**   :‖

21

I Fought The Law

Words & Music by
Sonny Curtis

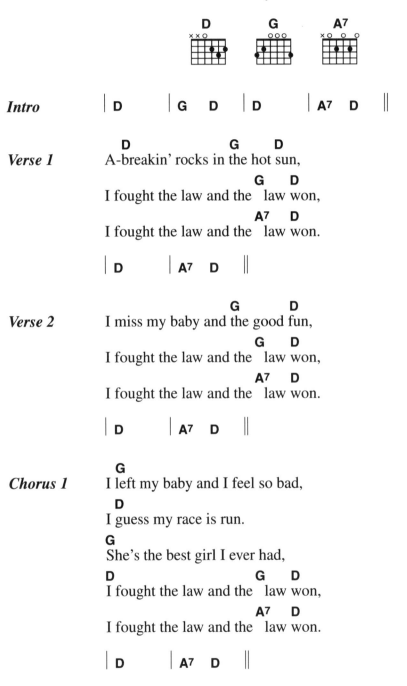

Intro | D | G D | D | A7 D ||

Verse 1

        D   **G**   **D**
A-breakin' rocks in the hot sun,
                    G   **D**
I fought the law and the law won,
                  A7 **D**
I fought the law and the law won.

| D | A7 D ||

Verse 2

                 G   **D**
I miss my baby and the good fun,
                  G   **D**
I fought the law and the law won,
                  A7 **D**
I fought the law and the law won.

| D | A7 D ||

Chorus 1

G
I left my baby and I feel so bad,
 D
I guess my race is run.
G
She's the best girl I ever had,
D   **G** **D**
I fought the law and the law won,
                  A7 **D**
I fought the law and the law won.

| D | A7 D ||

Verse 3

                                    G   **D**
A-robbin' people with a zip gun,

                           G   **D**
I fought the law and the law won,

                           A⁷   **D**
I fought the law and the law won.

 | **D** | **A⁷** **D**   ‖

Verse 4

                             G   **D**
I needed money 'cause I had none,

                           G   **D**
I fought the law and the law won,

                           A⁷   **D**
I fought the law and the law won.

 | **D** | **A⁷** **D**   ‖

Chorus 2

 G
I left my baby and I feel so bad,

 D
I guess my race is run.

G
She's the best girl I ever had,

D   **G**   **D**
I fought the law and the law won,

                           A⁷   **D**
I fought the law and the law won.

 | **D** | **A⁷** **D**   ‖

No Particular Place To Go

Words & Music by
Chuck Berry

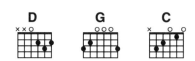

Verse 1	**D** **G**

Verse 1

    D   **G**
Ridin' along in my automobile,

My baby beside me at the wheel.
                             C
I stole a kiss at the turn of a mile,
                         G
My curiosity runnin' wild.
                                D
Cruisin' and playin' the radio,
                     G
With no particular place to go.

Verse 2

                                    G
Ridin' along in my automobile,

I was anxious to tell her the way I feel.
                         C
So I told her softly and sincere,
                                 G
And she leaned and whispered in my ear.
                         D
Cuddlin' more and drivin' slow,
                     G
With no particular place to go.

Solo 1 | G | G | G | G | C | C |

               | G | G | D | C | G | G ‖

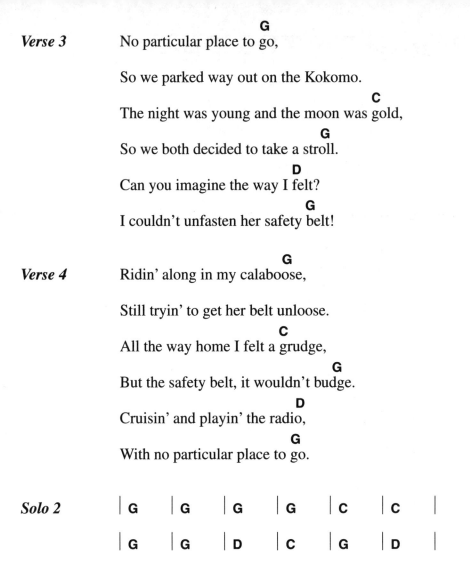

Verse 3

              G
No particular place to go,

So we parked way out on the Kokomo.

                                  C
The night was young and the moon was gold,

                      G
So we both decided to take a stroll.

                    D
Can you imagine the way I felt?

                    G
I couldn't unfasten her safety belt!

Verse 4

                    G
Ridin' along in my calaboose,

Still tryin' to get her belt unloose.

                  C
All the way home I felt a grudge,

                         G
But the safety belt, it wouldn't budge.

                    D
Cruisin' and playin' the radio,

                  G
With no particular place to go.

Solo 2

G	G	G	G	C	C	
G	G	D	C	G	D	
G	G	G	G	C	C	
G	G	D	C	G	G	‖

Power To The People

Words & Music by
John Lennon

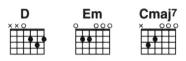

Intro

D	Em D Em	D

Power to the peo - ple!

D   Em D Em D
Power to the peo - ple!

D   Em D Em D
Power to the peo - ple!

D   Em D Em D
Power to the peo - ple!

Chorus 1

D   Em D Em D   Em D
Power to the peo - ple!

D   Em D Em D   Em D
Power to the peo - ple!

D   Em D Em D   Em D
Power to the peo - ple!

D   Cmaj7   D
Power to the people, right on!

Verse 1

D   Em
  You say you want a revolution,

We'd better get on it right away.

Well, let's get on your feet,

End of the street, singing:

Chorus 2

D   Em D Em D   Em D
Power to the peo - ple!

D   Em D Em D   Em D
Power to the peo - ple!

D   Em D Em D   Em D
Power to the peo - ple!

D   Cmaj7   D
Power to the people, right on!

Verse 2

D   Em
A million workers workin' for nothin',

You better give 'em what they really own.

We gotta put you down

When we come into town, singing:

Chorus 3

D   Em D Em D   Em D
Power to   the peo - ple!

D   Em D Em D   Em D
Power to   the peo - ple!

D   Em D Em D   Em D
Power to   the peo - ple!

D   Cmaj⁷   D
Power to the people, right on!

Verse 3

D   Em
I gotta ask you comrades and brothers,

How do you treat your old woman back home?

She's gotta be herself

So she can give us help, singing:

Chorus 4

D   Em D Em D   Em D
‖: Power to   the peo - ple!

D   Em D Em D   Em D
Power to   the peo - ple!

D   Em D Em D   Em D
Power to   the peo - ple!

D   Cmaj⁷   D
Power to the people, right on! :‖   *Repeat to fade*

Red, Red Wine

Words & Music by
Neil Diamond

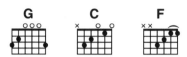

Verse 1

G C F
Red, red wine

G   C F
 Goes to my head,

G   C   F
 Makes me forget that I,

G
 Still need her so.

Verse 2

F G C F
Red, red wine

G   C F
 It's up to you.

G   C   F
 All I can do, I've done,

G
 Memories won't go,

F   G   C F
 Memories won't go.

Middle 1

G   C
 I'd have thought that with time,

F   C
Thoughts of you'd leave my head.

    G   C
I was wrong; now I __ find

       F   G
Just one thing makes me forget.

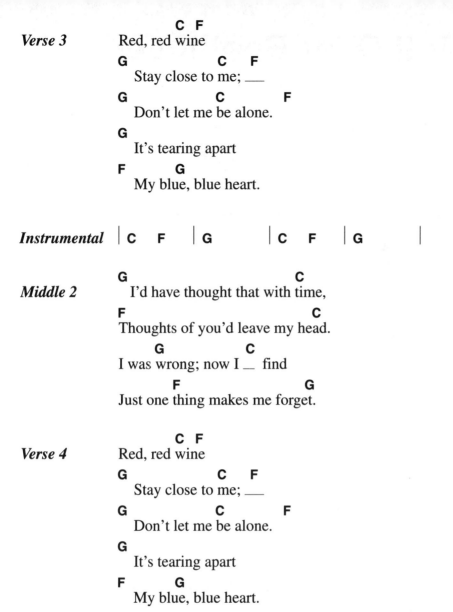

Verse 3

            C F
Red, red wine
  G   **C**   **F**
  Stay close to me; ___
  G   **C**   **F**
  Don't let me be alone.
  G
  It's tearing apart
  F   **G**
  My blue, blue heart.

Instrumental | **C** **F** | **G** | **C** **F** | **G** |

Middle 2

  G   **C**
  I'd have thought that with time,
F   **C**
Thoughts of you'd leave my head.
    G   **C**
I was wrong; now I __ find
        F   **G**
Just one thing makes me forget.

Verse 4

            C F
Red, red wine
  G   **C**   **F**
  Stay close to me; ___
  G   **C**   **F**
  Don't let me be alone.
  G
  It's tearing apart
  F   **G**
  My blue, blue heart.

Roll Over Beethoven

Words & Music by
Chuck Berry

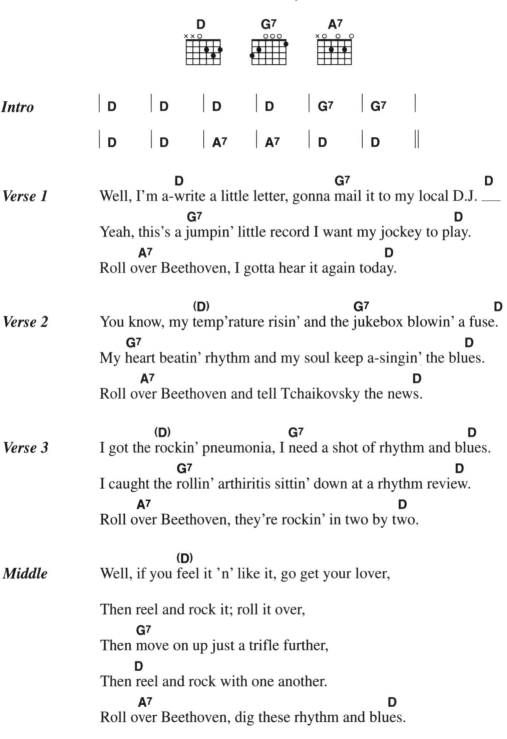

Intro

| D | D | D | D | G⁷ | G⁷ | |

| D | D | A⁷ | A⁷ | D | D | ‖ |

Verse 1

        D   **G⁷**   **D**
Well, I'm a-write a little letter, gonna mail it to my local D.J. ___
  G⁷   **D**
Yeah, this's a jumpin' little record I want my jockey to play.
  A⁷   **D**
Roll over Beethoven, I gotta hear it again today.

Verse 2

           (D)   **G⁷**   **D**
You know, my temp'rature risin' and the jukebox blowin' a fuse.
  G⁷   **D**
My heart beatin' rhythm and my soul keep a-singin' the blues.
  A⁷   **D**
Roll over Beethoven and tell Tchaikovsky the news.

Verse 3

         (D)   **G⁷**   **D**
I got the rockin' pneumonia, I need a shot of rhythm and blues.
    G⁷   **D**
I caught the rollin' arthiritis sittin' down at a rhythm review.
  A⁷   **D**
Roll over Beethoven, they're rockin' in two by two.

Middle

         (D)
Well, if you feel it 'n' like it, go get your lover,

Then reel and rock it; roll it over,
  G⁷
Then move on up just a trifle further,
  D
Then reel and rock with one another.
  A⁷   **D**
Roll over Beethoven, dig these rhythm and blues.

Solo | D | G⁷ | D | D | G⁷ | G⁷ |

| D | D | A⁷ | G⁷ | D | A⁷ ||

Verse 4

        D   **G⁷**
Well, early in the mornin' and I'm givin' you my warnin'

           D
Don't you step on my blue suede shoes.

G⁷
Hey diddle diddle, I'm a-playin' my fiddle,

D
   Ain't got nothin' to lose.

        A⁷   **D**
Roll over Beethoven and tell Tchaikovsky the news.

Verse 5

                   (D)
You know she wiggles like a glow worm,

G⁷   **D**
   Dance like a spinnin' top.

        G⁷   **D**
She got a crazy partner, you ought-a see 'em reel and rock.

        A⁷   **D**
Long as she got a dime the music will never stop.

Outro

             (D)
Roll over Beethoven,

Roll over Beethoven,

       G⁷
Roll over Beethoven,

       D
Roll over Beethoven,

       A⁷
Roll over Beethoven,

             D
Dig these rhythm and blues.

She Bangs The Drums

Words & Music by
Ian Brown & John Squire

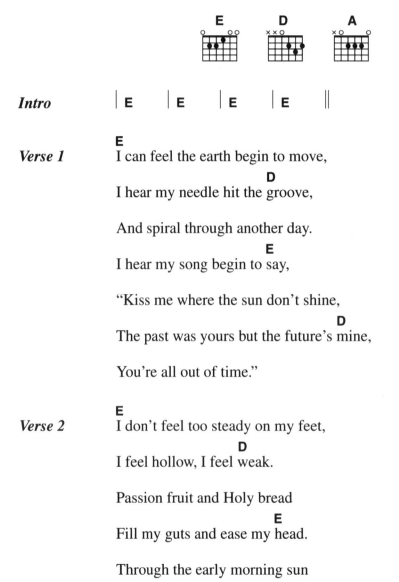

Intro | E | E | E | E ||

Verse 1

E
I can feel the earth begin to move,

D
I hear my needle hit the groove,

And spiral through another day.

E
I hear my song begin to say,

"Kiss me where the sun don't shine,

D
The past was yours but the future's mine,

You're all out of time."

Verse 2

E
I don't feel too steady on my feet,

D
I feel hollow, I feel weak.

Passion fruit and Holy bread

E
Fill my guts and ease my head.

Through the early morning sun

D
I can see her, here she comes,

She bangs the drums.

Chorus 1

```
A           D              A
Have you seen her, have you heard?
              D              A
The way she plays, there are no words
         D         E
To describe the way I feel.
A           D           A
How could it ever come to pass?
             D              A
She'll be the first, she'll be the last
            D         E
To describe the way I feel, the way I feel.
```

Instrumental | A | A | E | E | A | A | E | E |

| E | E | E | E | D | D | D | D |

| E | E | E | E | D | D | D | D E |

The way I feel.

Chorus 2   As Chorus 1

Chorus 3   As Chorus 1

Outro   ‖: A | D | A | D | A | D | E | E |

| A | D | A | D | A | D | E | E :‖

Repeat to fade

Summertime Blues

Words & Music by
Eddie Cochran & Jerry Capehart

Intro
| C F | G C | C F | G C ‖

Verse 1

          C
I'm a-gonna raise a fuss, I'm a-gonna raise a holler,

| C F | G C |
    (C)
About a-workin' all summer just to try to earn a dollar.

| C F | G C |
      F
Ev'ry time I call my baby, try to get a date,
      N.C.
My boss says, "No dice, son, you gotta work late,"
F
Sometimes I wonder what I'm a-gonna do,
        C   G C
But there ain't no cure for the summertime blues.

| C F | G C | C F | G C ‖

Verse 2

    (C)
A-well my Mom 'n' Papa told me, "Son, you gotta make some money,

| C F | G C |
    (C)
If you want-ta use the car to go a-ridin' next Sunday."

| C F | G C |
     F
Well, I didn't go to work, told the boss I was sick,
N.C.
"Now you can't use the car 'cause you didn't work a lick."

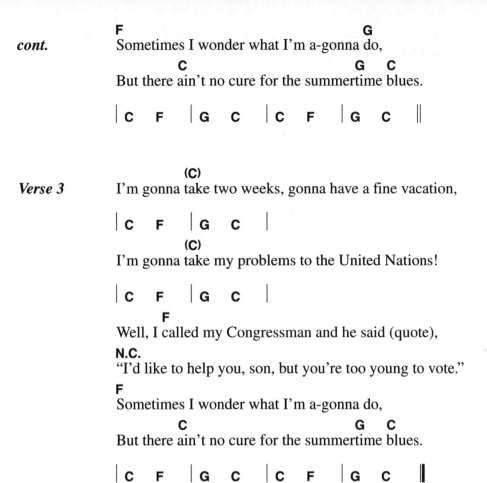

cont.

     F   **G**
Sometimes I wonder what I'm a-gonna do,

            C   **G** **C**
But there ain't no cure for the summertime blues.

C	F	G	C	C	F	G	C

Verse 3

             (C)
I'm gonna take two weeks, gonna have a fine vacation,

C	F	G	C

             (C)
I'm gonna take my problems to the United Nations!

C	F	G	C

       F
Well, I called my Congressman and he said (quote),
N.C.
"I'd like to help you, son, but you're too young to vote."
F
Sometimes I wonder what I'm a-gonna do,

            C   **G** **C**
But there ain't no cure for the summertime blues.

C	F	G	C	C	F	G	C

Sweet Little Sixteen

Words & Music by
Chuck Berry

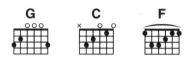

Chorus 1

N.C.   G   C
They're really rockin' in Boston, and Pittsburgh, P. A.

                           G   C
Deep in the heart of Texas and 'round the Frisco Bay.

         F   C
All over St. Louis, and down in New Orleans,

                   G   C
All the cats wanna dance with Sweet Little Sixteen.

Verse 1

(C)   G   C
   Sweet Little Sixteen, she's just got to have

          G   C
About half a million, a famed autograph.

                 F   C
Her wallet filled with pictures, she gets 'em one by one,

          G   C
Becomes so excited, watch-a look at her run, boy.

Bridge

         F   G
Oh Mammy, Mammy, please may I go?

            G   C
You're such a sight to see, somebody steal the show.

        F   C
Oh Daddy, Daddy, I beg of you,

         G   C
Whisper to Mammy, it's all right with you.

Chorus 2

(C)   G   C
   'Cause they'll be rockin' on the bandstand, in Philadelphia P. A.

                           G   C
Deep in the heart of Texas and 'round the Frisco Bay.

         F   C
All over St. Louis, way down in New Orleans,

                   G   C
All the cats wanna dance with Sweet Little Sixteen.

Solo | G | G | C | C | G | G | C | C |

          | F | F | C | C | G | G | C |

Chorus 3

(C)   G   C
'Cause they'll be rockin' on the bandstand, in Philadelphia P. A.
                     G   C
Deep in the heart of Texas and 'round the Frisco Bay.
                F   C
All over St. Louis, way down in New Orleans,
                    G   C
All the cats wanna dance with Sweet Little Sixteen.

Verse 2

(C)   G   C
Sweet Little Sixteen, she's got the grown up blues,
                G   C
Tight dresses and lipstick, she's sportin' high-heeled shoes.
                F   C
Oh, but tomorrow mornin' she'll have to change her trend,
                G   C
And be sweet sixteen, and back in class again.

Chorus 4

(C)   G   C
'Cause they'll be rockin' in Boston, and Pittsburgh, P. A.
                     G   C
Deep in the heart of Texas and 'round the Frisco Bay.
                F   C
Way out in St. Louis, way down in New Orleans,
                    G   C
All the cats wanna dance with Sweet Little Sixteen.

Thank U

Words by Alanis Morissette
Music by Alanis Morissette & Glen Ballard

C   G   F

Intro | C | C | G | F ||

Verse 1
C   G   F
How 'bout getting off o' those antibio - tics?
C   G   F
How 'bout stopping eating when I'm full up?
C   G   F
How 'bout them transparent dangling carrots?
C   G   F
How 'bout that ever elusive ku - do?

Chorus 1
                    C
Thank you India, thank you terror;
              G   F
Thank you dis - illusionment.
                    C
Thank you frailty, thank you consequence;
              G   F
Thank you, thank you silence.

Verse 2
C   G   F
How 'bout me not blaming you for ev'ry - thing?
C   G   F
How 'bout me enjoying the moment for once?
C   G   F
How 'bout how good it feels to fin'lly forgive you?
C   G   F
How 'bout grieving it all one at a time?

Chorus 2   As Chorus 1

Middle

       C
The moment I let go of it
          G   F
Was the mo - ment I got more than I __ could handle.
        C
The moment I jumped off of it
         G   F
Was the mo - ment I touched down.

Verse 3

       C   G   F
How 'bout no longer being masochistic?
       C   G F
How 'bout remembering your divinity?
       C   G   F
How 'bout unabashedly bawling your eyes out?
       C   G F
How 'bout not equating death with stopping?

Chorus 3

               C
‖: Thank you India, thank you providence;
            G   F
Thank you dis - illusionment.
               C
Thank you no - thingness, thank you clarity;
         G   F
Thank you, thank you silence. :‖ *Repeat to fade with ad lib vocal*

This Ole House

Words & Music by
Stuart Hamblen

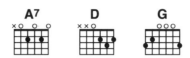

Intro | A⁷ | A⁷ | A⁷ | D ||

Verse 1

      D
This ole house once knew his children,
      G
This ole house once knew his wife,
      A⁷
This ole house was home and comfort,
      D   **G**   **D**
As they fought the storms of life.

This ole house once rang with laughter,
      G
This ole house heard many shouts,
      A⁷
Now he trembles in the darkness,
           D
When the lightnin' walks about.

Chorus 1

      G
Ain't a-gonna need this house no longer,
      D
Ain't a-gonna need this house no more,
      A⁷
Ain't got time to fix the shingles,
      D
Ain't got time to fix the floor.
      G
Ain't got time to oil the hinges,
      D
Nor to mend no windowpanes,
      A⁷
Ain't a-gonna need this house no longer,
           D
He's a-gettin' ready to meet his fate.

Verse 2

```
              D
This ole house is a-gettin' shaky,
              G
This ole house is a-gettin' old,
              A7
This ole house lets in the rain,
              D        G      D
This ole house lets in the cold.
```

```
Oh, his knees are a-gettin' chilly,
              G
But he feels no fear nor pain,
              A7
'Cause he seeks a new tomorrow,
                       D
Through a golden windowpane.
```

Chorus 2   As Chorus 1

Verse 3

```
              D
This ole house is afraid of thunder,
              G
This ole house is afraid of storms,
              A7
This ole house just groans and trembles,
              D        G      D
When the night wind flings its arms.
```

```
This ole house is a-gettin' feeble,
              G
This ole house is a-needin' paint,
              A7
Just like him it's tuckered out.
                       D
He's a-gettin' ready to meet his fate.
```

Chorus 3   As Chorus 1

Twist And Shout

Words & Music by
Bert Russell & Phil Medley

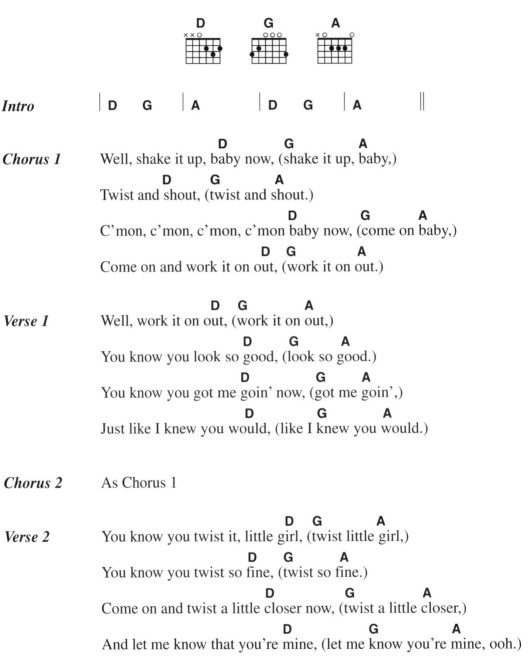

Intro

| D G | A | D G | A |

Chorus 1

                   D   **G**   **A**
Well, shake it up, baby now, (shake it up, baby,)
          D   **G**   **A**
Twist and shout, (twist and shout.)
                         D   **G** **A**
C'mon, c'mon, c'mon, c'mon baby now, (come on baby,)
                   D **G**   **A**
Come on and work it on out, (work it on out.)

Verse 1

                 D **G**   **A**
Well, work it on out, (work it on out,)
                D   **G**   **A**
You know you look so good, (look so good.)
                   D   **G** **A**
You know you got me goin' now, (got me goin',)
              D   **G**   **A**
Just like I knew you would, (like I knew you would.)

Chorus 2   As Chorus 1

Verse 2

                       D **G**   **A**
You know you twist it, little girl, (twist little girl,)
                 D **G**   **A**
You know you twist so fine, (twist so fine.)
                    D   **G**   **A**
Come on and twist a little closer now, (twist a little closer,)
                   D   **G**   **A**
And let me know that you're mine, (let me know you're mine, ooh.)

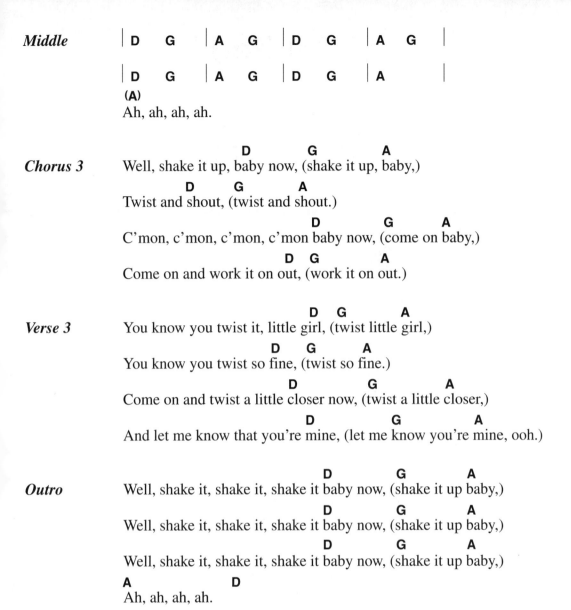

Middle
```
| D   G   | A   G   | D   G   | A   G   |
| D   G   | A   G   | D   G   | A       |
```
(A)
Ah, ah, ah, ah.

Chorus 3
                         D   **G**   **A**
Well, shake it up, baby now, (shake it up, baby,)
        D   **G**   **A**
Twist and shout, (twist and shout.)
                  D   **G**   **A**
C'mon, c'mon, c'mon, c'mon baby now, (come on baby,)
                D G   **A**
Come on and work it on out, (work it on out.)

Verse 3
                    D G   **A**
You know you twist it, little girl, (twist little girl,)
           D G   **A**
You know you twist so fine, (twist so fine.)
               D   **G**   **A**
Come on and twist a little closer now, (twist a little closer,)
               D   **G**   **A**
And let me know that you're mine, (let me know you're mine, ooh.)

Outro
                  D   **G**   **A**
Well, shake it, shake it, shake it baby now, (shake it up baby,)
                  D   **G**   **A**
Well, shake it, shake it, shake it baby now, (shake it up baby,)
                  D   **G**   **A**
Well, shake it, shake it, shake it baby now, (shake it up baby,)
A   **D**
Ah, ah, ah, ah.

Uninvited

Words & Music by
Alanis Morissette

D   Gm   G

Verse 1

D
Like anyone would be,

        Gm   D
I am flattered by your fascination with me.

Like any hot-blooded woman,

           Gm   D
I have simply wanted an object to crave.

      D   G
But you, you're not allowed;

          D
You're uninvited: an unfortunate slight.

Verse 2

(D)
Must be strangely exciting

          Gm   D
To watch the stoic squirm.

Must be somewhat heartening

           Gm   D
To watch shepherd meet shepherd.

      D   G
But you, you're not allowed;

          D
You're uninvited: an unfortunate slight.

Instrumental | D | D | D | D ||

Verse 3

    (D)
Like any uncharted territory,
      Gm   **D**
I must seem greatly intriguing.

You speak of my love
              Gm   **D**
Like you have experienced love like mine before.
    D   **G**
But this is not allowed;
           D
You're uninvited: an unfortunate slight.

Instrumental | D | D | D | D | D | D   ‖

I don't think you unworthy;
         Gm   **D**
I need a moment to deliberate.

Instrumental ‖: D | D | D | D   :‖ *Play 4 times*

             | D   ‖

Working Class Hero

Words & Music by
John Lennon

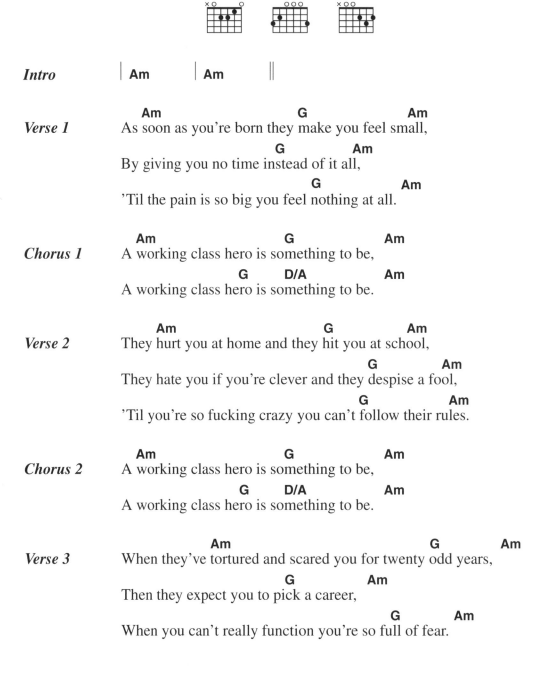

Intro | Am | Am ||

Verse 1
```
        Am                      G           Am
As soon as you're born they make you feel small,
                   G          Am
By giving you no time instead of it all,
                            G          Am
'Til the pain is so big you feel nothing at all.
```

Chorus 1
```
        Am                 G           Am
A working class hero is something to be,
              G      D/A       Am
A working class hero is something to be.
```

Verse 2
```
        Am                    G          Am
They hurt you at home and they hit you at school,
                          G            Am
They hate you if you're clever and they despise a fool,
                             G           Am
'Til you're so fucking crazy you can't follow their rules.
```

Chorus 2
```
        Am                 G           Am
A working class hero is something to be,
              G      D/A       Am
A working class hero is something to be.
```

Verse 3
```
             Am                              G        Am
When they've tortured and scared you for twenty odd years,
                 G          Am
Then they expect you to pick a career,
                            G        Am
When you can't really function you're so full of fear.
```

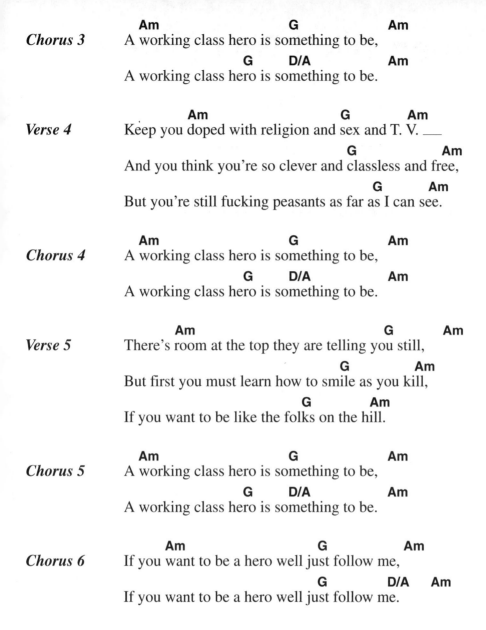

Chorus 3

    Am   G   Am
A working class hero is something to be,
                        G   D/A   Am
A working class hero is something to be.

Verse 4

                   Am   G   Am
Keep you doped with religion and sex and T. V. ___
                                    G   Am
And you think you're so clever and classless and free,
                                   G   Am
But you're still fucking peasants as far as I can see.

Chorus 4

    Am   G   Am
A working class hero is something to be,
                        G   D/A   Am
A working class hero is something to be.

Verse 5

           Am   G   Am
There's room at the top they are telling you still,
                              G   Am
But first you must learn how to smile as you kill,
                         G   Am
If you want to be like the folks on the hill.

Chorus 5

    Am   G   Am
A working class hero is something to be,
                      G   D/A   Am
A working class hero is something to be.

Chorus 6

        Am   G   Am
If you want to be a hero well just follow me,
                           G   D/A   Am
If you want to be a hero well just follow me.

When Will I Be Loved?

Words & Music by
Phil Everly

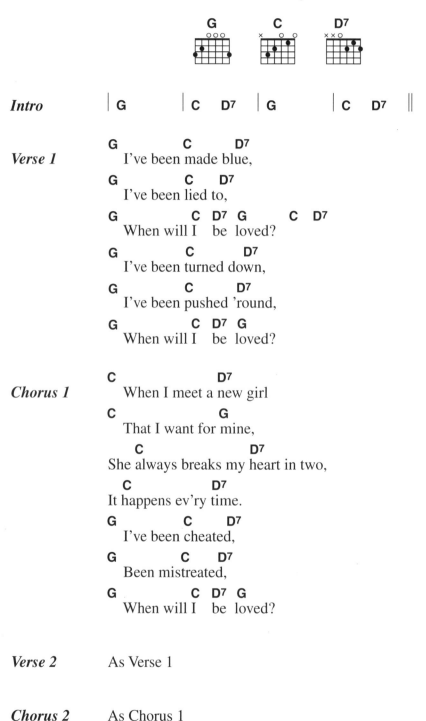

Intro | G | C   D7 | G | C   D7 ||

Verse 1

G   C   D7
I've been made blue,

G   C   D7
I've been lied to,

G   C D7 G   C D7
When will I be loved?

G   C   D7
I've been turned down,

G   C   D7
I've been pushed 'round,

G   C D7 G
When will I be loved?

Chorus 1

C   D7
When I meet a new girl

C   G
That I want for mine,

    C   D7
She always breaks my heart in two,

C   D7
It happens ev'ry time.

G   C   D7
I've been cheated,

G   C   D7
Been mistreated,

G   C D7 G
When will I be loved?

Verse 2   As Verse 1

Chorus 2   As Chorus 1

09/03 (48608)